James Herriot's
Animal Storybook

Other Books for Children
by James Herriot

Illustrated by Peter Barrett
MOSES THE KITTEN
ONLY ONE WOOF

Illustrated by Ruth Brown
OSCAR, CAT-ABOUT-TOWN
SMUDGE'S DAY OUT

James Herriot's
Animal Storybook

Illustrated by Ruth Brown

BCA
LONDON · NEW YORK · SYDNEY · TORONTO

This edition published 1992 by BCA by arrangement with Michael Joseph Ltd

Typeset in 14pt on 18pt Garamond Light
Printed in Hong Kong by Imago Publishing Limited

A CIP catalogue record for this book is available from the British Library

CN 8669

The moral right of the author has been asserted

Contents

Introduction

This is the first omnibus of my children's books and as I look through the pages I bless my luck yet again that they should be so brilliantly brought to life by Ruth Brown's illustrations.

When my adult books first became popular, I began to receive letters from all over the world and I soon realised that many of them came from children. These young people seemed to respond eagerly to the accounts of my experiences as a vet, confirming the truth that children have a special rapport with animals. They not only find them attractive - be it the family dog or cat, or animals on the farm - but they have an uncanny feeling for their needs and respond naturally to the unswerving affection which the animals dispense.

I know that I write again and again about the care of these four-legged creatures who share and enhance our lives; after all, that is what a vet's life is about. Most animals are totally vulnerable and are therefore wholly dependent on our kindness and willingness to look after them and this, I believe, is at the root of the deep pull they have upon our emotions. They can be pretty, funny, charming in a thousand ways, but behind it all is the unalterable fact that they rely utterly on us to care for them, and when we betray that faith with neglect or cruelty their reaction is one of bewilderment.

When I began to write books especially for children, the letters I received reflected their intense interest and affection for the animals, in particular when the creatures concerned were in any form of distress. I regularly receive packets of letters from school classes, each one telling me about the things which appealed most to them in the books, touched them or made them laugh, and I derive great help and satisfaction from reading them and looking at the little drawings which are often sent as well.

My own children were devoted to their pets and found great pleasure in accompanying me on my veterinary rounds, and now my grandchildren who are growing up with yet another generation of cats and dogs are discovering that special happiness which comes from loving and being loved by all creatures great and small.

James Herriot

The
Christmas Day
Kitten

Christmas can never go by without my remembering a certain little cat. I first saw her when I called to see one of Mrs Pickering's much-loved Basset hounds.

I looked in some surprise at the furry creature moving quietly down the hall.

'I didn't know you had a cat,' I said to Mrs Pickering, who was a plumpish, pleasant-faced woman.

Mrs Pickering smiled. 'We haven't really. Debbie is a stray. She comes here two or three times a week and we give her some food. I don't know where she lives.'

'Do you ever get the feeling that she wants to stay with you?' I asked.

'No.' Mrs Pickering shook her head. 'She's a timid little thing. Just creeps in, has some food, then slips away. She doesn't seem to want to let me help her in any way.'

I looked at the little tabby cat again. 'But she isn't just having food today.'

'It's a funny thing, but every now and again she pops through into the sitting-room and sits by the fire for a few minutes. It's as though she was giving herself a treat.'

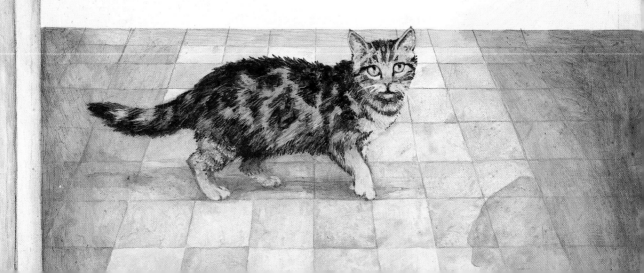

The little cat was sitting very upright on the thick rug which lay in front of the fireplace in which the coals glowed and flamed. The three Bassets were already lying there but they seemed used to Debbie because two of them sniffed her in a bored manner and the third merely cocked a sleepy eye at her before flopping back to sleep.

Debbie made no effort to curl up or wash herself or do anything other than gaze quietly ahead. This was obviously a special event in her life, a treat.

Then suddenly she turned and crept from the room without a sound, and was gone.

'That's just the way it is with Debbie,' said Mrs Pickering, laughing. 'She never stays more than ten minutes or so, then she's off.'

I often visited the Pickering home and I always looked out for the little cat. On one occasion I spotted her nibbling daintily from a saucer at the kitchen door. As I watched, she turned and almost floated on light footsteps into the hall, then through into the sitting-room.

Debbie settled herself in the middle of the pile of Basset hounds in her usual way: upright, still, and gazing into the glowing fire.

This time, I tried to make friends with her but she leaned away as I stretched out my hand. However, I talked to her softly and I managed to stroke her cheek with one finger.

Then it was time for her to go and, once outside the house, she jumped up on to the stone wall and down the other side. The last I saw was the little tabby figure flitting away across the grassy field.

'I wonder where she goes?' I murmured.

'That's something we've never been able to find out,' said Mrs Pickering.

It was three months later that I next heard from Mrs Pickering –
and it happened to be Christmas morning.

'I'm so sorry to bother you today of all days,' said Mrs Pickering
apologetically.

'Don't worry at all,' I said. 'Which of the dogs needs attention?'

'It's not the dogs. It's … Debbie. She's come to the house and
there's something very wrong. Please come quickly.'

I drove through the empty market square. The snow was thick on the road and on the roofs of the surrounding houses. The shops were closed but the pretty coloured lights of the Christmas trees winked in the windows.

Mrs Pickering's house was beautifully decorated with tinsel and holly, and the rich smell of turkey and sage and onion stuffing wafted from the kitchen. But she had a very worried look on her face as she led me through to the sitting-room.

Debbie was there, but she wasn't sitting upright in her usual position. She was lying quite still – and huddled close to her lay a tiny kitten.

I looked down in amazement. 'What have we got here?'
    'It's the strangest thing,' Mrs Pickering replied. 'I haven't
seen her for several weeks and then she came in about two
hours ago, staggered into the kitchen, and she was carrying
the kitten in her mouth. She brought it in here and laid it on
the rug. Almost immediately I could see that she wasn't well.
Then she lay down like this and she hasn't moved since.

I knelt on the rug and passed my hand over Debbie's body which Mrs Pickering had placed on a piece of sheet. She was very, very thin and her coat was dirty. I knew that she didn't have long to live.

'Is she ill, Mr Herriot?' asked Mrs Pickering in a trembling voice.

'Yes … yes, I'm afraid so. But I don't think she is in any pain.'

Mrs Pickering looked at me and I saw there were tears in her eyes. Then she knelt beside Debbie and stroked the cat's head while the tears fell on the dirty fur.

Oh, the poor little thing! I should have done more for her.'

I spoke gently. 'Nobody could have done more than you. Nobody could have been kinder. And see, she has brought her kitten to you, hasn't she?'

'Yes, you are right, she has.' Mrs Pickering reached out and lifted up the tiny, bedraggled kitten. 'Isn't it strange – Debbie knew she was dying so she brought her kitten here. And on Christmas Day.'

I bent down and put my hand on Debbie's heart. There was no beat. 'I'm afraid she has died.' I lifted the feather-light body, wrapped it in the piece of sheet and took it out to the car.

When I came back, Mrs Pickering was still stroking the kitten. The tears had dried, and she was bright-eyed as she looked at me.

'I've never had a cat before,' she said.

I smiled. 'Well, it looks as though you've got one now.'

And she certainly had. The kitten grew rapidly into a sleek, handsome and bouncy tabby cat and Mrs Pickering called him Buster. He wasn't timid like his little mother and he lived like a king – and with the ornate collar he always wore, looked like one too.

I watched him grow up with delight, but the occasion that always stays in my mind was the following Christmas Day, a year after his arrival.

I was on my way home after visiting a farmer with a sick cow, and I was looking forward to my Christmas dinner. Mrs Pickering was at her front door when I passed her house and I heard her call out, 'Merry Christmas, Mr Herriot! Come in and have a drink to warm you up.'

I had a little time to spare, so I stopped the car and went in. In the house there was all the festive cheer of last year and the same glorious whiff of sage and onion stuffing. But this year, there was no sorrow – there was Buster!

He was darting up to each of the Basset hounds in turn, ears pricked, eyes twinkling, dabbing a paw at them, and then streaking away.

Mrs Pickering laughed. 'Buster does tease them so. He gives them no peace.'

She was right. For a long time, the dogs had led a rather sedate life: gentle walks with their mistress, plenty of good food, and long snoring sessions on the rugs and armchairs. Then Buster arrived.

He was now dancing up to the youngest dog again, head on one side, asking him to play. When he started boxing with both paws, it was too much for the Basset who rolled over with the cat in a wrestling game.

'Come into the garden,' said Mrs Pickering. 'I want to show you something.'

She lifted a hard rubber ball from the sideboard and we went outside.

She threw the ball across the lawn and Buster bounded after it over the frosty grass, his tabby coat gleaming in the sun. He seized the ball in his mouth, brought it back to his mistress, dropped it at her feet, and waited. Mrs Pickering threw it and again Buster brought it back.

I gasped. A retriever-cat!

The Bassets looked on unimpressed. Nothing would ever make *them* chase a ball, but Buster did it again and again as though he would never tire of it.

Mrs Pickering turned to me. 'Have you ever seen anything like that?'

'No,' I replied. 'He is a most remarkable cat.'

We went back into the house where she held Buster close to her, laughing as the big cat purred loudly. Looking at him, so healthy and contented, I remembered his mother who had carried her tiny kitten to the only place of comfort and warmth that she had ever known.

Mrs Pickering was thinking the same thing because she turned to me and, although she was smiling, her eyes were thoughtful. 'Debbie would be pleased,' she said.

I nodded. 'Yes, she would. It was just a year ago today she brought him in, wasn't it?'

'That's right.' She hugged Buster again. 'The best Christmas present I've ever had.'

Bonny's Big Day

One sunny morning in early September, I drove to see
old John Skipton at Dale Close Farm since he had
telephoned to say that one of his carthorses was lame.

As I got out of the car, the untidily-dressed figure of the farmer came through the kitchen door of Dale Close.

John always seemed to look like a scarecrow, and today was no different. He was wearing a tattered buttonless coat which was tied round his waist with string. His trousers were much too short and, as he hurried towards me, I could see that he was wearing socks of different colours – one was red, and the other was blue.

By working very hard when he was a young man, Mr Skipton had saved enough money to buy his own farm with its handsome stone house. He had never married and because he was always so busy looking after the sheep and cows on the hill, bringing in the harvest from the fields, and picking the apples in the orchard, he had been much too busy to worry about himself – which is why he was always dressed in such very old clothes.

'The horses are down by the river,' he said in his usual gruff manner. 'We'll have to go down there.' He seized a pitchfork and stabbed it into a big pile of hay which he then hoisted on to his shoulder. I pulled my large Gladstone bag from the car and set off behind him.

It was difficult to keep up with the farmer's brisk pace even though he must have been fifty years older than me. I was glad when we reached the bottom of the hill because the bag was heavy and I was getting rather hot.

I saw the two horses standing in the shallows of the pebbly river. They were nose to tail, and were rubbing their chins gently along each other's backs. Beyond them, a carpet of green turf ran up to a high sheltered ridge, while all around clumps of oak and beech blazed in the autumn sunshine.

'They're in a nice place, Mr Skipton,' I said.

'Aye, they can keep cool in the hot weather, and they've got the barn when the winter comes.'

At the sound of his voice, the two big horses came trotting up from the river – the grey one first, and the chestnut following a little more slowly, and limping slightly.

They were fine big carthorses, but I could see they were old from the sprinkling of white hairs on their faces. Despite their age, however, they pranced around old John, stamping their enormous feet, throwing their heads about and pushing the farmer's cap over his eyes with their muzzles.

'Get over, leave off!' he cried.

He pulled at the grey horse's forelock. 'This is Bonny, she's well over twenty years old.' Then he ran his hand down the front leg of the chestnut. 'And this is Dolly. She's nearly thirty now, and not one day's sickness until now.'

'When did they last do any work?' I asked.

'Oh, about twelve years ago, I reckon,' the farmer replied.

I stared at him in amazement. 'Twelve years? Have they been down here all that time?'

'Aye, just playing about down here. They've earned their retirement.'

For a few seconds he stood silent, shoulders hunched, hands deep in the pockets of his tattered coat.

'They worked very hard when I had to struggle to get this farm going,' he murmured, and I knew he was thinking of the long years those horses had pulled the plough, drawn the hay and harvest wagons, and had done all the hard work which the tractors now do.

'I noticed that Dolly was a bit lame when I came down with their hay yesterday,' he said. 'Lucky I come down each day.'

'You mean that you climb down that hillside every single day?' I asked.

'Aye – rain, wind or snow. They look forward to me bringing a few oats or some good hay.'

I examined Dolly's foot and found an old nail embedded deep in the soft part of her foot. I was able to pull it out quite easily with a pair of pincers, and then gave her an antitetanus injection to eliminate any risk of later infection.

Climbing back up the hill, I couldn't help thinking how wonderful it was that old John had made the long journey to see the horses in all weathers, every day for twelve years. He certainly loved those great animals.

A thought struck me, and I turned to him. 'You know, Mr Skipton, it's the Darrowby Show next Saturday. You should enter the mares in the Family Pets Class. I know they are asking for unusual entries this year. Perhaps you should only take Bonny since Dolly's foot will be a bit sore for a few days.'

The farmer frowned. 'What on earth are you talking about?'

'Go on,' I said. 'Take Bonny to the show! Those horses are your pets, aren't they?'

'Pets!' he snorted. 'You couldn't call one of those great big clod-hoppers a pet. I've never heard anything so silly.'

When he got back to the farmyard, he thanked me gruffly, gave me a nod and disappeared into his house.

The following Saturday, it was my duty to attend Darrowby Show as the vet-in-charge. I had spent a pleasant time strolling around the showground, looking at the pens of cattle and sheep, the children's ponies, the massive bulls, and the sheepdog trials in the neighbouring fields.

Then over the loudspeaker came the following announcement: 'Would the entrants for the Family Pets Class please take their places in the ring.'

I was always interested in this event, so I walked over and stood by the Secretary who was sitting at a table near the edge of the ring. He was Darrowby's local bank manager, a prim little man with rimless spectacles and a pork pie hat. I could see that he was pleased at the number of entrants now filing into the ring.

He looked at me and beamed. 'They have certainly taken me at my word when I asked for unusual entries this year.'

The parade was led by a fine white nanny goat which was followed by a pink piglet. Apart from numerous cats and dogs of all shapes and sizes, there was a goldfish in its bowl, and at least five rabbits. There was a parrot on a perch, and some budgies having an outing in their cage. Then to an excited buzz of conversation, a man walked into the ring with a hooded falcon on his wrist.

'Splendid, splendid!' cried Mr Secretary – but then his mouth fell open and everyone stopped talking as a most unexpected sight appeared.

Old John Skipton came striding into the ring, and he was leading Bonny – but it was a quite different man and horse than I had seen a few days before.

John still wore the same old tattered coat tied with string, but today I noticed that both his socks were the same colour and on his head, perched right in the centre, was an ancient bowler hat.

It made him look almost smart, but not as smart as Bonny. She was dressed in the full show regalia of an old-fashioned carthorse. Her hooves were polished and oiled, the long feathery hair on her lower limbs had been washed and fluffed out; her mane, tail and forelock had been plaited with green and yellow ribbons, and her coat had been groomed until it shone in the sunshine. She was wearing part of the harness from her working days and it, too, had been polished, and little bells hung from the harness saddle.

It quite took my breath away to look at her.

'Mr Skipton, Mr Skipton! You can't bring that great thing in here. This is the class for Family Pets!' cried Mr Secretary leaping up from his chair.

'Bonny *is* my pet,' responded the farmer. 'She's part of my family. Just like that old goat over there.'

'Well, I disagree,' said Mr Secretary, waving his arms. 'You must take her out of the ring, and go home.'

Old John Skipton put on a fierce face and glared at the man. 'Bonny *is* my pet,' he repeated. 'Just ask Mr Herriot.'

I shrugged my shoulders. 'Perfectly true. This mare hasn't worked for over twelve years and is kept entirely for Mr Skipton's pleasure. I'd certainly call Bonny a pet.'

'But...but...' spluttered Mr Secretary. Then he sat down suddenly on his chair, and sighed, 'Oh, very well then, go and get into line.'

So John turned and led Bonny to a place right in the middle of the other competitors. On one side of them was the little pink piglet, and on the other side a tortoise. It was a most curious sight.

The task of judging the pets had been given to the district nurse who was very sensibly dressed in her official uniform to give her an air of authority. Judging this class was always difficult, and when she looked along the line and kept seeing the great horse, she knew it was going to be very difficult indeed.

She looked carefully at every competitor, but her eyes always came back to Bonny. All the rabbits were very sweet, the falcon was impressive, the dogs were charming, and the piglet was cute – but Bonny was *MAGNIFICENT!*

'First prize to Mr Skipton and Bonny,' she announced and everyone cheered.

As the rosette was presented, a man came to take a photograph for the local newspaper. It looked as though the great horse knew all about her prize as she posed there, dignified and beautiful. John too stood very erect and proud – but, unfortunately, every time the photographer clicked the camera, Bonny pushed the bowler hat over the farmer's eyes.

It was the mare's way of showing her love, but I couldn't help wondering how the picture would come out.

After the show, I went back to Dale Close to help John 'undress' Bonny – and I went with them down the hill to the field by the river.

As we approached, Dolly came trotting up from the river, whinnying with pleasure to see her friend and companion again.

'Her foot is quite healed now,' I said, noting the horse's even stride.

In the gentle evening light we watched the two old horses hurry towards each other. Then for a long time, they stood rubbing their faces together.

'Look at that,' said old John with one of his rare smiles. 'Bonny is telling Dolly all about her big day!'

Bonny takes first prize in the Family Pets class
(The Darrowby and Houlton Times)

Blossom
Comes Home

I arrived at Mr Dakin's farm just outside Darrowby on a warm April morning. The green hillside ran down to the river, and the spring sunshine danced on the water. The birds were singing and lambs played on the flower-strewn pastures.

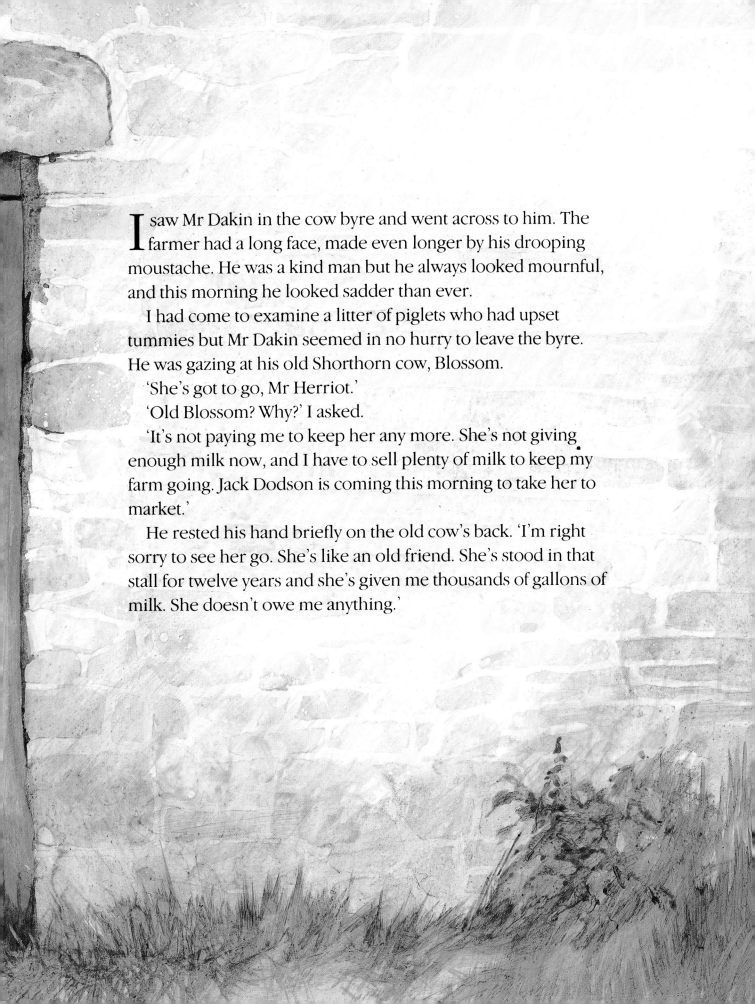

I saw Mr Dakin in the cow byre and went across to him. The farmer had a long face, made even longer by his drooping moustache. He was a kind man but he always looked mournful, and this morning he looked sadder than ever.

I had come to examine a litter of piglets who had upset tummies but Mr Dakin seemed in no hurry to leave the byre. He was gazing at his old Shorthorn cow, Blossom.

'She's got to go, Mr Herriot.'

'Old Blossom? Why?' I asked.

'It's not paying me to keep her any more. She's not giving enough milk now, and I have to sell plenty of milk to keep my farm going. Jack Dodson is coming this morning to take her to market.'

He rested his hand briefly on the old cow's back. 'I'm right sorry to see her go. She's like an old friend. She's stood in that stall for twelve years and she's given me thousands of gallons of milk. She doesn't owe me anything.'

There were only six cows in the old cobbled byre with its low roof and wooden partitions, and they all had names. You don't find cows with names any more, and there aren't many farmers like Mr Dakin who somehow scratch a living from a herd of six milking cows and a few calves, pigs and hens.

As if she knew she was the topic of conversation, Blossom turned her head and looked at him. She was certainly very ancient: her pelvic bones jutted out from her skinny body and her udder drooped almost to the ground. But there was something appealing in the friendliness of the eyes and the patient expression on her face.

Mr Dakin had fallen silent as he looked fondly at his cow. I was about to suggest that we might see the piglets when I heard a clattering of boots in the yard and Jack Dodson, the drover, hurried into the byre.

'Now then, Mr Dakin,' he cried. 'It's easy to see which one you want me to take. It's that skinny old thing over there.'

He pointed to Blossom and, in truth, the unkind description seemed to fit the bony creature standing among her sleek neighbours.

The farmer didn't reply for a moment, then he went between the cows and gently rubbed Blossom's forehead. 'Aye, this is the one, Jack.' Then he undid the chain round her neck. 'Off you go, old lass,' he murmured, and the cow turned and made her way placidly from the stall.

'Come along, come along!' shouted Jack Dodson, prodding the cow's rump.

'Don't hit her!' barked Mr Dakin.

Mr Dodson looked at him in surprise. 'I never hit 'em, you know that. Just help 'em along, like.'

'All right,' Mr Dakin replied. 'But you won't need your stick for this one. She'll go wherever you want, always has done.'

Blossom proved him right and ambled across the yard. She turned up the track to join a group of fat bullocks and cows standing on the road high above. A boy and a dog circled them, keeping them together.

The farmer and I stood watching as Blossom made her way unhurriedly up the hill, Jack Dodson following behind her. As the path wound behind an old grey barn, man and beast disappeared – but Mr Dakin still gazed after them, listening to the clip-clop of the hooves on the hard ground.

When the sound had died away, he turned to me quickly. 'Right, Mr Herriot, we'll get on with seeing those little pigs.'

There were twelve squealing piglets in the sty with their
mother. The farmer gently picked each one up and held it
while I gave it an injection which would make it better. This took
me about fifteen minutes and I tried to pass the time by talking
about the weather, cricket and other things, but Mr Dakin replied
only with a series of grunts. I could see that he was still sad about
Blossom.

I, too, was thinking about the old cow as I drove away from the farm, up the track and on to the road above. On my way home, I had to pass through the nearby village of Briston, and as I arrived, I saw the herd of cattle at the far end of the street. Mr Dodson was making another collection, and the boy was chatting to some friends by the roadside. I could see Blossom at the rear of the group, with her head turned, looking back.

Briston was where Mrs Pickering lived with her three Basset hounds and Buster, the cat who was once her Christmas Day kitten. One of the dogs had broken his leg a month before and I had to remove the plaster cast this morning.

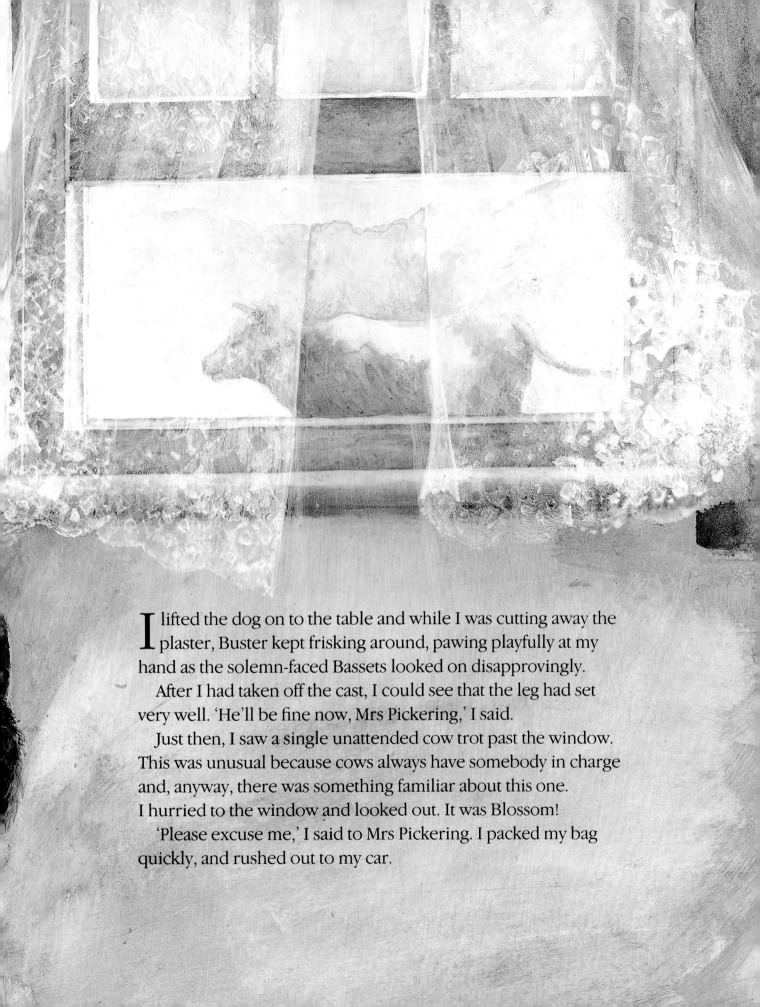

I lifted the dog on to the table and while I was cutting away the plaster, Buster kept frisking around, pawing playfully at my hand as the solemn-faced Bassets looked on disapprovingly.

After I had taken off the cast, I could see that the leg had set very well. 'He'll be fine now, Mrs Pickering,' I said.

Just then, I saw a single unattended cow trot past the window. This was unusual because cows always have somebody in charge and, anyway, there was something familiar about this one. I hurried to the window and looked out. It was Blossom!

'Please excuse me,' I said to Mrs Pickering. I packed my bag quickly, and rushed out to my car.

Blossom was moving down the village street at a good pace, her eyes fixed steadily ahead as though she was going somewhere important. What on earth had happened? She should have been at Darrowby market by now. People in the street were staring at her and the postman nearly fell off his bike as she pushed past him. Then she disappeared round the corner and out of sight.

I had to turn the car, and then I drove after her at top speed – but when I rounded the corner, there was no sign of her, and the road that stretched ahead of me was empty. She had vanished – but where had she gone?

One thing was certain. I had to go back to Mr Dakin's farm and tell him that Blossom had broken away and was loose in the countryside.

I urged my little car as fast as I could and when I reached the farm, I met Mr Dakin carrying a sack of grain across the yard.

He looked at me in surprise. 'Hello, Mr Herriot. Have you forgotten something?'

I was about to blurt out my story when he raised his head suddenly, and listened. 'What's that?' he said.

From somewhere on the hillside above us, I could hear the clip-clop of hooves. As we stood in the yard and listened, a cow rounded a rocky outcrop and came towards us. It was Blossom, moving at a brisk trot, great udder swinging, eyes fixed purposefully on the byre door.

'What on earth. . .' burst out Mr Dakin, but the old cow brushed past us and marched without hesitation into the stall she had occupied for the past twelve years. She sniffed enquiringly at the empty hay rack and looked round at her astonished owner.

Mr Dakin stared back at her. The eyes in the weathered face were watery, and he began to pull thoughtfully at his long moustache.

The silence was broken by the sound of heavy boots on the cobbles of the yard, and Jack Dodson panted his way through the door.

'Oh, there you are, you old scallywag!' he gasped. 'I'm right sorry, Mr Dakin. I left that lad in charge for a few minutes and he let her escape.' Then he moved towards Blossom. 'Come on, lass, let's be having you out of there.'

But he halted as Mr Dakin held an arm in front of him.

There was a long silence as Dodson looked in surprise
at the farmer who continued to gaze at the cow.
There was a quiet dignity about the old animal as she
stood there against the crumbling timbers of the
partition, her eyes patient and undemanding.

Then, still without speaking, Mr Dakin moved
unhurriedly between the cows and the faint click of
metal sounded as he fastened the chain around Blossom's
neck. Next he strolled to the end of the byre and returned
with a forkful of hay which he tossed expertly into the
wooden rack.

This was what Blossom was waiting for. She snatched
a mouthful and began to chew with quiet satisfaction.

'What's going on?' cried Jack Dodson in bewilderment. 'I'll be late for market.'

'I'm sorry I've wasted your time, Jack,' the farmer replied slowly, 'but you'll have to go without her.'

'Without her... but...?' spluttered Mr Dodson.

'Aye, you'll think I'm daft, but that's how it is. The old lass has come home and she's staying home.'

Mr Dodson shook his head, and left the byre to get back to the market.

'Mr Herriot,' he said, 'do you ever feel that sometimes when unexpected things happen, they were meant to, and that it works out for the best in the end?'

'Yes,' I said, 'I often think that.'

'Well, that's how I felt when Blossom came back down the hill.' He reached out and scratched the old cow's back. 'She's always been my favourite and I'm glad she's back.'

I was still puzzled. 'But I can't understand how she got here. Why didn't I see her on the road? Where did she disappear to?'

A smile spread slowly across Mr Dakin's face, and he pulled again at his long moustache. 'Oh, there's another way to the farm. A little path which starts near the village.'

'And Blossom knows that path?'

'Oh aye, the old girl knows everything about this place.'

I looked at the six cows in a row. 'Didn't you say that you couldn't afford to keep her?' I asked, worried.

'That's right, but I've had an idea,' the farmer replied. 'I can put two or three calves on to her instead of milking her. The old stable across the yard is empty and she can live in there quite happily.'

'What a wonderful idea, Mr Dakin. She'll be very comfortable there and she'd suckle three calves easily. She would probably pay her way.'

'Well, I'm not worried about that,' said the farmer smiling. 'After all these years, she doesn't owe me anything. The important thing is that Blossom has come home.'

The
Market Square
Dog

On market days I used to take a walk across the cobbled
square to meet the farmers who gathered there to chat.
One of the farmers was telling me about his sick cow when we
saw the little dog among the market stalls. The thing that made
us notice the dog was that he was sitting up, begging, in front
of the stall selling cakes and biscuits.

'Look at that little chap,' the farmer said. 'I wonder where he's
come from?'

As he spoke, the stallholder threw him a bun which the dog devoured eagerly, but when the man came round and stretched out a hand the little animal trotted away. He stopped, however, at another stall which sold eggs, butter, cheese and scones. Without hesitation, he sat up again in the begging position, rock steady, paws dangling, head pointing expectantly.

I nudged my companion. 'There he goes again.
I always think a dog looks very appealing sitting up like that.'
    The farmer nodded. 'Yes, he's a bonny little thing, isn't he?
What breed would you call him?'
    'A cross, I'd say. He's like a small sheepdog, but there's a
touch of something else – maybe terrier.'

It wasn't long before the dog was munching a biscuit, and this time I walked over to him, and as I drew near I spoke gently. 'Here, boy,' I said, squatting down in front of him. 'Come on, let's have a look at you.'

He turned to face me, and for a moment two friendly brown eyes gazed at me from a wonderfully attractive face. The fringed tail waved in response to my words, but as I moved nearer he turned and trotted away among the market-day crowd until he was lost to sight.

I was standing there, trying to see where he had gone, when a young policeman came up to me.

'I've been watching that wee dog begging among the stalls all morning,' he said, 'but, like you, I haven't been able to get near him.'

'Yes, it's strange. You can see he's friendly, but he's also afraid. I wonder who owns him.'

'I reckon he's a stray, Mr Herriot. I'm interested in dogs myself and I fancy I know just about all of them around here. But this one is a stranger to me.'

I nodded. 'I'm sure you're right. Anything could have happened to him. He could have been ill-treated by somebody and run away, or he could have been dumped from a car.'

'Yes,' the policeman replied, 'there are some cruel people about. I don't know how anybody can leave a helpless animal to fend for itself like that. I've had a few tries at catching him, but it's no good.'

The memory stayed with me for the rest of the day. It is our duty to look after the animals who depend on us and it worried me to think of the little creature wandering about in a strange place, sitting up and asking for help in the only way he knew.

Market day is on a Monday and on the Friday of that week my wife Helen and I had a treat in store; we were going to the races in Brawton. Helen was making up a picnic basket with home-made ham-and-egg-pie, chicken sandwiches and a chocolate cake. I was wearing my best suit and I couldn't help feeling very smart because country vets have to work mostly in the fields and cowsheds and I hardly ever got dressed up. Helen, too, had put on her best dress and a fancy hat I had never seen before. As a vet's wife, she too had to work very hard and we weren't able to go out together very often.

We were just about to leave the house when the doorbell rang. It was the young policeman I had been talking to on market day.

'I've got that dog, Mr Herriot,' he said. 'You know – the one that was begging in the market square.'

'Oh good,' I replied, 'so you managed to catch him at last.'

The policeman paused. 'No, not really. One of our men found him lying by the roadside about a mile out of town and brought him in. I'm afraid he's been knocked down. We've got him here in the car.'

I went out and looked into the car. The little dog was lying very still on the back seat, but when I stroked the dark coat his tail stirred briefly.

'He can still manage a wag, anyway,' I said.

The policeman nodded. 'Yes, there's no doubt he's a good-natured wee thing.'

I tried to examine him as much as possible without touching because I didn't want to hurt him, but I could see that he had cuts all over his body and one hind leg lay in such a way that I knew it must be broken. When I gently lifted his head, I saw that one eyelid was badly torn so that the eye was completely closed. But the other soft brown eye looked at me trustingly.

'Can you do anything for him, Mr Herriot?' asked the policeman. 'Can you save him?'

'I'll do my best,' I replied.

I carried the little animal into the surgery and laid him on the table.

'There's an hour or two's work here, Helen,' I said to my wife. 'I'm very sorry, but we won't be able to go to the races.'

'Never mind,' she replied. 'We must do what we can for this fellow.'

Rather sadly she took off her fancy hat and I took off my good jacket. Dressed in our white coats we began to work.

Helen was used to helping me and she gave the anaesthetic, then I set the broken leg in plaster and stitched up the wounds. The worst thing was the eye because even after I had stitched the eyelid it was still bruised and tightly closed and I was worried that he might lose the sight in that eye.

By the time we had finished, it was too late to go out anywhere, but Helen was quite cheerful. 'We can still have our picnic,' she said.

We carried the sleeping dog out to the garden and laid him on a mat on the lawn so that we could watch him as he came round from the anaesthetic.

Out there in the old high-walled garden the sun shone down on the flowers and the apple trees. Helen put on her fancy hat again and I put my smart jacket back on and as we sat there, enjoying the good things from the picnic basket, we felt that we were still having a day out. But Helen kept glancing anxiously at the little dog and I knew she was thinking the same thing as I was. Would he be all right after all that we had done for him and, even then, what was going to happen to him? Would his owners ever come to claim him, because if they didn't, he had nobody in the world to look after him.

Since he was a stray dog, he had to go into the kennels at the police station and when I visited him there two days later, he greeted me excitedly, balancing well on his plastered leg, his tail swishing. All his fear seemed to have gone. I was delighted to see that the injured eye was now fully open, and the swelling down.

The young policeman was as pleased as I was. 'Look at that!' he exclaimed. 'He's nearly as good as new again.'

'Yes,' I said, 'he's done wonderfully well.' I hesitated for a moment. 'Has anybody enquired about him?'

He shook his head. 'Nothing yet, but we'll keep hoping, and in the meantime we'll take good care of him here.'

I visited the kennels often, and each time the shaggy little creature jumped up to greet me, laughing into my face, mouth open, eyes shining. But nobody seemed to want him.

After a few more days it was clear that no owner was going to claim him, and my only hope was that somebody else would take him and give him a home.

There were other stray dogs in the kennels, and on one visit I saw a farmer calling to collect his wandering sheepdog.

Then a family was overjoyed at being reunited with their handsome golden retriever.

Finally a little old lady came in and tearfully gathered her tiny Yorkshire terrier into her arms. But nobody came for my little patient.

Various strangers came too, looking for a pet, but nobody seemed to be interested in him. Maybe it was because he was only a mongrel and the people who visited the kennels wanted a more elegant dog – yet I knew that he would make a perfect pet for anybody.

A week passed before I went again to the police station. The little dog's kennel was empty.

'What's happened?' I asked the policeman. 'Has somebody taken him?'

The policeman looked very grave. 'No,' he replied, 'I'm afraid he's been arrested.'

'Arrested?' I said in astonishment. 'What do you mean?'

'Well,' he said, 'it seems that it's against the law for a dog to go begging in the market square so he has been taken into police custody.'

I was bewildered. 'What are you talking about? A dog can't be arrested.'

The policeman, still very solemn, shrugged his shoulders. 'This dog was.'

'I still don't know what this is all about,' I said. 'Where is he now?'

'I'll take you to him,' the policeman replied.

We left the police station and walked a short way along the road to a pretty cottage.

We went inside and there, in the sitting-room, curled up in a big new doggy bed was my little friend. Two small girls were sitting by his side, stroking his coat.

The policeman threw back his head and laughed. 'I've just been kidding you, Mr Herriot. This is my house and I've taken him as a pet for my two daughters. They've been wanting a dog for some time and I've got so fond of this wee chap that I thought he'd be just right for them.'

A wave of relief swept over me. 'Well, that's wonderful,' I said and I looked at his kind face gratefully. 'What's your name?' I asked.

'Phelps,' he replied. 'PC Phelps. And they call me Funny Phelps at the police station because I like playing jokes on people.'

'Well, you certainly took me in,' I said. 'Arrested indeed!'

He laughed again. 'Well, you've got to admit he's in the hands of the law now!'

I laughed too. I didn't mind having the joke played on me because, funny Phelps or not, he was obviously a nice Phelps and would be a kind master for my doggy friend.

It was a happy day when I took the plaster off the little dog's leg and found that the break had healed perfectly. All the nasty cuts had healed, too, and when I lifted him down from the table, the small girls held up a beautiful new red collar with a lead to match. Their new pet liked the look of them because he sat up in that position I remembered so well, his paws dangling, his face looking up eagerly. The begging dog had found a home at last.

James Herriot has just retired as a practising vet after more than fifty years of devoted work. Although his favourite animals are dogs and cats he has spent much of his life caring for cattle, sheep, pigs and horses on the Yorkshire farms. He is married and has two children: Jimmy, who is now senior partner in the veterinary practice, and Rosie who is a doctor.

James Herriot has written many bestselling books about his life as a vet in the beautiful Yorkshire Dales, and his latest book, *Every Living Thing*, has just been published. He has written eight books for children, six of them gloriously illustrated by Ruth Brown. James Herriot and his wife live in a village in the North Yorkshire hills - imagining no other place they would rather be.